CHRISTMAS PLANNER

PERSONAL INFORMATION

CARDS SENT AND RECEIVED

CARDS SENT AND RECEIVED

NAME & ADDRESS	SENT	RECEIVED

CARDS SENT AND RECEIVED

NAME & ADDRESS	SENT	RECEIVED

CARDS SENT AND RECEIVED

NAME & ADDRESS	SENT	RECEIVED

CARDS SENT AND RECEIVED

NAME & ADDRESS	SENT	RECEIVED

CARDS SENT AND RECEIVED

NAME & ADDRESS	SENT	RECEIVED

CARDS SENT AND RECEIVED

NAME & ADDRESS	SENT	RECEIVED

CARDS SENT AND RECEIVED

NAME & ADDRESS	SENT	RECEIVED

CARDS SENT AND RECEIVED

NAME & ADDRESS	SENT	RECEIVED

CARDS SENT AND RECEIVED

NAME & ADDRESS	SENT	RECEIVED

GIFTS TO BUY

GIFTS TO BUY

NAME	IDEA/GIFT	COST

GIFTS TO BUY

NAME	IDEA/GIFT	COST

GIFTS TO BUY

NAME	IDEA/GIFT	COST

GIFTS TO BUY

NAME	IDEA/GIFT	COST

GIFTS TO BUY

NAME	IDEA/GIFT	COST

GIFTS TO BUY

NAME	IDEA/GIFT	COST

GIFTS TO BUY

NAME	IDEA/GIFT	COST

GIFTS TO BUY

NAME	IDEA/GIFT	COST

GIFTS TO BUY

NAME	IDEA/GIFT	COST

GIFTS TO BUY

NAME	IDEA/GIFT	COST

GIFTS TO BUY

NAME	IDEA/GIFT	COST

SHOPPING LISTS

SHOPPING LISTS

ITEM	DONE

ITEM	DONE

SHOPPING LISTS

ITEM	DONE

ITEM	DONE

SHOPPING LISTS

ITEM	DONE

ITEM	DONE

SHOPPING LISTS

ITEM	DONE

ITEM	DONE

SHOPPING LISTS

ITEM	DONE

ITEM	DONE

SHOPPING LISTS

ITEM	DONE

ITEM	DONE

SHOPPING LISTS

ITEM	DONE

ITEM	DONE

SHOPPING LISTS

ITEM	DONE

ITEM	DONE

SHOPPING LISTS

ITEM	DONE

ITEM	DONE

SHOPPING LISTS

ITEM	DONE

ITEM	DONE

SHOPPING LISTS

ITEM	DONE

ITEM	DONE

CHRISTMAS OVERVIEW

CHRISTMAS OVERVIEW

TIMES	23 DECEMBER	24 DECEMBER	25 DECEMBER

CHRISTMAS OVERVIEW

TIMES	26 DECEMBER	27 DECEMBER	28 DECEMBER

CHRISTMAS OVERVIEW

TIMES	23 DECEMBER	24 DECEMBER	25 DECEMBER

CHRISTMAS OVERVIEW

TIMES	26 DECEMBER	27 DECEMBER	28 DECEMBER

NOTES

MEAL
PLANNER

DAY . . .

23RD DECEMBER

MEAL	TIMING	FOOD
BREAKFAST		
LUNCH		
DINNER		

DAY . . .

CHRISTMAS EVE

MEAL	TIMING	FOOD
BREAKFAST		
LUNCH		
DINNER		

DAY . . .

CHRISTMAS DAY

MEAL	TIMING	FOOD
BREAKFAST		
LUNCH		
DINNER		

DAY . . .

BOXING DAY

MEAL	TIMING	FOOD
BREAKFAST		
LUNCH		
DINNER		

DAY . . .

27 DECEMBER

MEAL	TIMING	FOOD
BREAKFAST		
LUNCH		
DINNER		

DAY . . .

28 DECEMBER

MEAL	TIMING	FOOD
BREAKFAST		
LUNCH		
DINNER		

DAY . . .

29 DECEMBER

MEAL	TIMING	FOOD
BREAKFAST		
LUNCH		
DINNER		

DAY . . .

30 DECEMBER

MEAL	TIMING	FOOD
BREAKFAST		
LUNCH		
DINNER		

DAY . . .

NEW YEAR'S EVE

MEAL	TIMING	FOOD
BREAKFAST		
LUNCH		
DINNER		

DAY . . .

NEW YEAR'S DAY

MEAL	TIMING	FOOD
BREAKFAST		
LUNCH		
DINNER		

DAY . . .

2 JANUARY

MEAL	TIMING	FOOD
BREAKFAST		
LUNCH		
DINNER		

DAY . . .

3 JANUARY

MEAL	TIMING	FOOD
BREAKFAST		
LUNCH		
DINNER		

TEMPERATURE CONVERSIONS

GAS MARK	FAHRENHEIT	CENTIGRADE	AGA SETTING
¼	225°F	110°C	VERY COOL
½	250°F	120°C	VERY COOL
1	275°F	135°C	VERY COOL
2	300°F	150°C	COOL
3	325°F	165°C	WARM
4	350°F	180°C	WARM
5	375°F	190°C	MEDIUM
6	400°F	200°C	MEDIUM / HIGH
7	425°F	220°C	MEDIUM / HIGH
8	450°F	230°C	HIGH
9	475°F	250°C	VERY HIGH

RECIPES

RECIPE :

INGREDIENTS :

METHOD :

RECIPE :

INGREDIENTS :

METHOD :

RECIPE :

INGREDIENTS :

METHOD :

RECIPE :

INGREDIENTS :

METHOD :

RECIPE :

INGREDIENTS :

METHOD :

RECIPE :

INGREDIENTS :

METHOD :

RECIPE :

INGREDIENTS :

METHOD :

RECIPE :

INGREDIENTS :

METHOD :

RECIPE :

INGREDIENTS :

METHOD :

RECIPE :

INGREDIENTS :

METHOD :

RECIPE :

INGREDIENTS :

METHOD :

RECIPE :

INGREDIENTS :

METHOD :

RECIPE :

INGREDIENTS :

METHOD :

RECIPE :

INGREDIENTS :

METHOD :

RECIPE :

INGREDIENTS :

METHOD :

RECIPE :

INGREDIENTS :

METHOD :

RECIPE :

INGREDIENTS :

METHOD :

RECIPE :

INGREDIENTS :

METHOD :

RECIPE :

INGREDIENTS :

METHOD :

RECIPE :

INGREDIENTS :

METHOD :

RECIPE :

INGREDIENTS :

METHOD :

RECIPE :

INGREDIENTS :

METHOD :

RECIPE :

INGREDIENTS :

METHOD :

RECIPE :

INGREDIENTS :

METHOD :

RECIPE :

INGREDIENTS :

METHOD :

RECIPE :

INGREDIENTS :

METHOD :

RECIPE :

INGREDIENTS :

METHOD :

RECIPE :

INGREDIENTS :

METHOD :

RECIPE :

INGREDIENTS :

METHOD :

RECIPE :

INGREDIENTS :

METHOD :

RECIPE :

INGREDIENTS :

METHOD :

CHRISTMAS REFLECTIONS

WHAT WENT WELL :

WHAT COULD BE IMPROVED FOR NEXT YEAR :

WHERE CHRISTMAS EVE WAS SPENT . . .

WHO WAS THERE . . .

WHAT HAPPENED . . .

WHERE CHRISTMAS DAY WAS SPENT . . .

WHO WAS THERE . . .

WHAT HAPPENED . . .

WHERE BOXING DAY WAS SPENT . . .

WHO WAS THERE . . .

WHAT HAPPENED . . .

WHERE NEW YEAR'S EVE/DAY WAS SPENT . . .

WHO WAS THERE . . .

WHAT HAPPENED . . .

CHRISTMAS PLANNER

First published by **FROM YOU TO ME** January 2017.

FROM YOU TO ME are committed to a sustainable future for our business, our customers and our planet. This book is printed and bound in China on FSC® certified paper.

MIX
Paper | Supporting responsible forestry
FSC® C005748

3 5 7 9 11 13 15 14 12 10 8 6 4

ISBN 978-1-907860-16-4

FROM YOU TO ME LTD, STUDIO 100, THE OLD LEATHER FACTORY
GLOVE FACTORY STUDIOS, HOLT, WILTSHIRE, BA14 6RJ